EDWARD ELGAR

ENIGMA VARIATIONS

for Orchestra
Op. 36

Ernst Eulenburg Ltd

London · Mainz · Madrid · New York · Paris · Prague · Tokyo · Toronto · Zürich

CONTENTS

PREFACE

Edward Elgar inscribed the autograph of his *Variations on an Original Theme for Orchestra*, Op.36, 'Ended Feb. 19th 1899'. Two days later he sent the score to the famous Wagnerian conductor Hans Richter. Richter was known to conduct only works for which he had a high regard: the *Variations* appeared in his next London concert, on 19 June 1899. The work was enthusiastically received, and has remained a favourite in the orchestral repertoire. This was a significant achievement on Elgar's part, since in the whole of Queen Victoria's reign no English orchestral work had so engaged the attention of the musical community. After the first performance, August Jaeger, Elgar's close friend and mentor (who is represented in the 'Nimrod' variation), wrote to Elgar suggesting that the finale was too short. Elgar was reluctant to change it; he explained that G major was 'exhausted' and that 'it wouldn't do to bring [the theme] in again'. But during the next few weeks he added 100 bars at the point just following fig. 76, and told Jaeger that he was pleased with the work's new 'tail'.[1]

The success of the *Variations* was not only a triumph for English music, it was also a personal achievement for Elgar because it marked the beginning of a new, international appreciation of his compositions. The *Variations* were played in Europe, and by the autumn of 1904 they had reached Russia. In the decade preceding the *Variations*, Elgar's main works had been written for chorus and orchestra. These include *The Black Knight* (1892), *The Light of Life* (1896), *King Olaf* (1896) and *Caractacus* (1898) which were performed at musical festivals in England and had helped to consolidate his national reputation. One commentator has mentioned that the greatest enigma of the *Variations* is that it sprang from a composer who, until the

age of 42, had not produced a masterpiece.[2] Another has suggested that, after the 'loosely narrative' choral works, Elgar realised his need for the 'discipline' of variations,[3] although the relationship between the theme and the variations can hardly be said to be strict in the Classical sense.

In 1904 Elgar was knighted. This honour has contributed to our picture of Elgar as the most 'English' of composers, a picture which is paradoxical, since Elgar's particular genius transcended rather than grew out of the music of his English predecessors and contemporaries, and his successors either adapted (Bliss, Walton) or reacted against (Holst, Vaughan Williams) his often explicitly 19th-century forms and compositional techniques. This is not to say that forward-looking tendencies cannot be discerned in Elgar's music: Richard Strauss dubbed him 'the first English progressivist musician'.

Foreign influences are not hard to identify in the *Variations*. It is worth considering, for instance, the question of genre. Viennese composers had written variations as the finales of symphonies (Haydn, Beethoven) or of concertos (Mozart), but the genre of independent orchestral variations was conceived in the 19th century. Although Elgar might have thought of Parry's *Symphonic Variations* (1897) whilst composing his own, better-known models for orchestral variations or variations for orchestra and solo instrument were written by Brahms, Dvoák, Franck and Tchaikovsky. Nineteenth-century tone poems, for example by Liszt, Smetana and Richard Strauss, may also have been a stimulus for Elgar's *Variations*, along with Schumann's musical ciphers and, perhaps above all, Wagner's music dramas, for the extra-musical associations of the *Variations* are indisputable.

[1] Basil Maine, *Elgar: his life and works*, 2 Vols. (London, 1933), Vol.1, *The Life*, 86–7

[2] Jack Westrup, 'The Enigma III' in Christopher Redwood (ed.), *An Elgar Companion* (London, 1982), 85

[3] Diana M. McVeagh, 'Elgar' in Stanley Sadie (ed.), *The New Grove Dictionary of Music and Musicians*, Vol.6 (London, 1980), 121

Elgar dedicated this work 'to my friends pictured within' and, above the music on the first page of the autograph full score, he later added the word 'Enigma'. Thus the *Variations* became known as the 'Enigma Variations', even though Elgar did not refer to it by this title in his correspondence. So what is the Enigma? Interest was initially fuelled by Elgar's programme notes to the first performance:

The Enigma I will not explain – its 'dark saying' must be left unguessed, and I warn you that the apparent connection between the Variations and the Theme is often of the slightest texture; further, through and over the whole set another and larger theme 'goes', but is not played.[4]

Elgar seemed increasingly unwilling to furnish further clues or give unambiguous answers to those who thought they had solved the puzzle. The 'dark saying' has been interpreted in diverse ways. It has been said to refer to the 'elegiac character' of the theme and to Elgar's sense of the loneliness of the artist when he wrote the *Variations*. It might reflect Elgar's view of himself ('just like me and my influence on everybody – always evil'[5]) and it has been observed that the rhythm of the opening phrase represents the name 'Edward Elgar' in natural speech rhythm. The *Variations* were perhaps even inspired by a passage from the Vulgate version of Corinthians which contains the word 'dark' in one translation.

The 'larger theme' that 'goes' has been understood to be a theme that is never stated but which is an implied counterpoint to the existing theme; *Auld Lang Syne* has been the most popular guess, though many others have been suggested. Some scholars have reservations about this approach because a 'hidden tune' that went with the theme would be unlikely to fit with all of the variations and, in any case, Elgar's statement does not necessarily imply that the large theme is a specific tune. The 'large theme' may

be a reference to friendship (appropriately enough if the hidden tune is *Auld Lang Syne*), it may recall a general musical experience such as the music of J.S.Bach, or Elgar might have consciously decided to embed Bach's name in the theme which begins with B (B$\flat$) and ends with H (B$\natural$) with A and C marked *tenuto* between these points.[6]

Whilst it is unlikely that all aspects of Elgar's enigma will ever be solved, Elgar did prove willing to reveal the names of his 'friends pictured within', disguised in the score by initials or pseudonyms above each of the variations.[7] He drew musical sketches of 12 of his friends, his wife and himself:

I. (C.A.E.) Elgar's wife, Alice.
II. (H.D.S-P.) Hew David Steuart-Powell, the pianist in a trio with Elgar and Basil Nevison. The variation portrays his 'characteristic diatonic runs over the keys'.
III. (R.B.T.) Richard Baxter Townshend, an Oxford eccentric; this section recalls his 'low voice flying off occasionally into "soprano" timbre'.
IV. (W.M.B.) William Meath Baker, who '[…] read out the arrangements for the day and hurriedly left the music-room with an inadvertent bang of the door'.
V. (R.P.A.) Richard Penrose Arnold, son of the poet, Matthew Arnold; 'whimsical & witty'.
VI. (Ysobel) Isabel Fitton, a viola player who had to practise leaps across the strings.
VII. (Troyte) Arthur Troyte Griffith: the drums represent his 'maladroit essays to play the pianoforte'.
VIII. (W.N.) Winifred Norbury: this variation is really a picture of her peaceful 18th-century house.
IX. (Nimrod) August Johannes Jaeger (Jaeger is German for Hunter, thus 'Nimrod'); Elgar wrote to Jaeger that 'I have omitted your out-

---

[4] D.M.Powell, *Edward Elgar: Memories of a Variation* (London, 1937, 3/1949), 121
[5] Michael Kennedy, *Elgar Orchestral Music* (London, 1970), 22
[6] Five influential articles which have contributed to this debate are reprinted in Redwood, op. cit., 50–90
[7] Quotations in this paragraph are from Elgar himself. For a more detailed discussion of the extra-musical references in the *Variations*, see Ian Parrott, *Elgar* (London, 1971), chapter 7.

side manners and have only seen the good, lovable honest SOUL in the middle of you'.

X. (Dorabella) Dora Penny. Elgar's nickname for her was Dorabella; he explained that this name was a quotation from Mozart's *Così fan tutte*. She had a stammer.

XI. (G.R.S.) George Robertson Sinclair, appointed organist of Hereford Cathedral in 1899. 'The variation has nothing to do with organs or cathedrals, or, except remotely, with G.R.S. The first few bars were suggested by his great bulldog, Dan.'

XII. (B.G.N.) Basil Nevison. 'A tribute to a very dear friend.'

XIII. (***) This is the only variation to be headed by asterisks. Elgar allowed his biographers to suppose that the dedicatee was Lady Mary Lygon, a musical friend, and indeed at first he placed the initials L.M.L. at the head of his account of the variations in his draft for the notes he published in 1913.[8] It has been suggested recently that the person enshrined in the music is the beautiful and brilliant American, Julia Worthington, who may have been Elgar's secret love.[9] The haunting clarinet quotation from Mendelssohn's Op.27, *Calm Sea and Prosperous Voyage*, perhaps conspires towards the mystery.

XIV. (E.D.U.) This is the composer himself; Edu was the name by which he was known to Alice.

In view of the intense concern with Elgar's epigrammatic references to the enigmas of his *Variations*, it is well to recall the composer's own feelings on this subject:

there is nothing to be gained in an artistic or musical sense by solving the engima of any of the personalities; the listener should hear the music as music, and not trouble himself with any intricacies of 'programme'. To me, the various personalities have been a source of inspiration, their idealisations a pleasure – and one that is intensified as the years go by.[10]

The score of the *Variations* was first published by Novello of London in 1899. Elgar's autograph full score is in the British Library, London, shelf-mark *GB-Lbl* Add. MS 59004.

Esther Cavett-Dunsby

[8] Edward Elgar, *My Friends Pictured Within* (London, 1913)

[9] Reed, 'Elgar's Enigmatic Inamorata', in *The Musical Times*, Vol.CXXV/1698 (August, 1984), 430–4

[10] Maine, op. cit., *The Works*, 102

VORWORT

Edward Elgar datierte die Beendigung seines Manuskripts der *Variations on an Original Theme for Orchestra*, op. 36 mit dem 19. Februar 1899. Zwei Tage darauf übersandte er die Partitur dem berühmten Wagner-Dirigenten Hans Richter. Dieser war dafür bekannt, nur solche Werke zu dirigieren, die er persönlich hoch einschätzte; die Variationen wurden in seinem nächsten Londoner Konzert gegeben, und zwar am 19. Juni 1899. Das Werk fand begeisterte Aufnahme und hat sich in England als eines der beliebtesten Repertoirestücke behauptet. Für Elgar seinerseits war es ein bahnbrechender Erfolg, zumal während der Regentschaft von Queen Victoria kein Orchesterwerk auf eine so rege Anteilnahme von Seiten der musikalischen Öffentlichkeit stieß. August Jaeger, Elgars enger Freund und Mentor (dem man in der 9. Variation, der „Nimrod Variation", begegnet), äußerte brieflich seine Ansicht, das Finale wäre wohl zu kurz geraten. Der einer Änderung sich widersetzende Elgar meinte daraufhin, die Tonart G-Dur wäre „ausgezehrt", „es würde nichts dabei herausspringen, das Thema noch einmal zu bringen". Dennoch schob er in den folgenden Wochen 100 neue Takte nach Ziffer 76 ein und meinte zu Jaeger, er wäre nun doch zufrieden mit dem hinzukomponierten „Schwanz" des Werkes.[1]

Der Erfolg der *Enigma-Variationen* war nicht allein ein absoluter Höhepunkt in der englischen Musikgeschichte, sondern auch – wie erwähnt – Elgars persönlicher Durchbruch, da sie den Ausgangspunkt für seine internationale Reputation als Komponist darstellten. Die Variationen gelangten nach Europa und im Herbst 1904 bis nach Russland. In den zehn Jahren vor ihrer Komposition schrieb Elga seine Hauptwerke für Chor und Orchester. Darunter sind *The Black Knight* (1892), *The Light of Life* (1896), *King*

Olaf (1896) und *Caractacus* (1898), die allesamt auf Musikfestivals in England aufgeführt wurden und dazu beitrugen, dass Elgar national zu Ansehen kam. Ein Rezensent äußerte, das größte Wunder der *Enigma-Variationen* sei, dass sie aus der Feder eines Komponisten geflossen seien, der bis zum Alter von 42 Jahren kein eigentliches Meisterwerk hervorgebracht hätte.[2] Ein weiterer Rezensent stellte die Vermutung an, dass Elgar nach den eher „erzählenden" Chorwerken einen Zwang zur „disziplinierenden" Variationenform verspürt hätte,[3] obgleich die Verwandtschaft zwischen dem Thema und den Variationen im eigentlichen klassischen Sinne nicht auszumachen sei.

1904 wurde Elgar zum Ritter geschlagen. Diese Auszeichnung hat er für heute in England noch gültige Begriffe dem Image zu verdanken, dass er als der „englischste" Komponist angesehen wurde – paradox insofern, als Elgars besonderes Talent eher unvermutet Grenzen überschritt, als dass es dem Boden der Werke seiner komponierenden englischen Vorgänger und Zeitgenossen entsprossen wäre. So kam es auch dazu, dass die Nachfolger Elgars häufig für das 19. Jahrhundert typische Formen und Kompositionstechniken gleichermaßen übernahmen (Bliss, Walton) wie von sich wiesen (Holst, Vaughan Williams). Dennoch kann nicht gleich die Rede davon sein, dass Elgars vorwärts weisende Ansätze keine Perspektive hätten: Richard Strauss versah Elgar mit dem Prädikat, „der fortschrittlichste aller Musiker in England" zu sein.

Der Einfluss von Komponisten anderer Länder ist unschwer herauszuhören. Bei Elgars Variationen sollte die Frage nach der Gattung erhoben werden. Die Komponisten der Wiener Klassik wählten für die Finale ihrer Sinfonien

[1] Basil Maine, „The life", in: *Elgar: his life and works*, 2 Bde., London 1933, S. 86f.

[2] Jack Westrup, „The Enigma III", in: Christopher Redwood (Hrsg.), *An Elgar Companion*, London 1982, S. 85.
[3] Diana M. McVeagb, „Elgar", in: Stanley Sadie (Hrsg), *The New Grove Dictionary of Music and Musicians*, Band 6, London 1980, S. 121.

mitunter die Variationsform (Haydn, Beethoven), ebenso in Konzerten (Mozart), doch schlug die Geburtsstunde für eigenständige Orchestervariationen erst im 19. Jahrhundert. Mag sein, dass Elgar bei seiner Komposition die *Symphonic Variations* von Parry (1897) im Sinn hatte – weitaus bekanntere Vorbilder für Orchestervariationen, auch für solche mit Klavier, waren von Brahms, Dvořák, Franck und Tschaikowsky bereits vorgegeben. Überdies ist auch der Einfluss von sinfonischen Dichtungen des 19. Jahrhunderts, z. B. von Seiten Liszts, Smetanas und Richard Strauss' sowie Schumanns musikalische Chiffren, als Antrieb für Elgars *Enigma-Variationen* denkbar, ganz zu schweigen von Wagners Musikdramen, die für die außermusikalischen Assoziationen der Variationen nicht wegzudenken sind.

Elgar widmete das Werk „meinen Freunden, die darin porträtiert sind". Zu einem späteren Zeitpunkt schrieb er über die erste autographe Notenseite das Wort „Enigma" (Rätsel), wodurch die Variationen als *Enigma-Variationen* bekannt wurden, auch wenn Elgar diesen Titel brieflich nie erwähnte. Was ist denn nun das „Rätsel"? Das Interesse an dieser Frage wurde ursprünglich durch Elgars Programmnotizen zur Uraufführung angefacht:

Zum „Rätsel" mag ich mich nicht weiter äußern – die düstere Grundhaltung des Werkes soll unerahnt bleiben, und ich mache darauf aufmerksam, dass die Ableitung der Variationen aus dem Thema oft lediglich andeutenden Charakter hat; weiterhin bildet sich im Verlauf der Sätze ein anderes, längeres Thema aus, das aber nicht ausgespielt wird.[4]

Anscheinend nahm Elgars Unwille, weiterführende Anhaltspunkte oder unzweideutige Antworten zugeben, um das Rätselspiel zu beenden, mehr und mehr zu. Die „düstere Grundhaltung" wurde unterschiedlich gedeutet. Man sprach davon, dass sie auf den „elegischen Charakter" des Themas und auch auf Elgars Gefühl der Einsamkeit des Schaffenden zur Zeit der Komposition zurückzuführen sei. In den *Enigma-*

Variationen könnte sich Elgars Selbsteinschätzung widerspiegeln („gerade wie ich und mein Einfluss auf jedermann – durchweg schlecht"[5]) und es ist die Feststellung gemacht worden, dass der Rhythmus der Eröffnungsphrase den Namen Edward Elgar im natürlichen Sprachrhythmus wiedergibt. Vielleicht handelt es sich auch um eine Inspiration durch eine Passage der Korintherbriefe in der Version der Vulgata des Wortes „düster" (oder „dunkel") in einer bestimmten Übersetzung.

Das „längere Thema", das „sich ausbildet", wurde als ein Thema aufgefasst, das sich niemals endgültig ausformt, aber ein mit einbegriffener Kontrapunkt zum Thema ist; *Auld Lang Syne* (ein schottisches Lied über Freundschaft) war hierbei die am häufigsten ausgesprochene Vermutung, obwohl auch anderes im Gespräch war. Einige Wissenschaftler meldeten gegen diesen Ausgangspunkt Bedenken an, dass eine „verborgene Melodie", dem Thema beigesellt, kaum mit allen Variationen in Einklang zu bringen sei. Jedenfalls geht aus Elgars Erklärung nicht hervor, dass das „lange Thema" ein ganz bestimmtes wäre. Es kann die Referenz an eine Freundschaft sein (überaus naheliegend, wenn es sich beim verborgenen Thema um *Auld Lang Syne* handelt), eine grundlegende musikalische Erfahrung – vergleichbar der Musik Johann Sebastian Bachs – oder bewusster Entschluss Elgars, Bachs Name in das mit B beginnende und mit H endende Thema einzubetten, versehen mit einem hervorgehobenen tenuto auf A und C zwischen diesen Polen.[6]

In der Erkenntnis, dass alle Aspekte seines Rätsels niemals erfasst werden würden, war Elgar bereit, die Namen seiner „porträtierten" Freunde preiszugeben, die er in der Partitur hinter Initialen oder Pseudonymen über jeder Variation versteckt hatte.[7] Er skizzierte zwölf

---

[4] D. M. Powell, *Edward Elgar: Memories of a Variation*, London 1937, 1949, S. 121.

[5] Michael Kennedy, *Elgar Orchestral Music*, London 1970, S. 22.

[6] Fünf grundlegende Artikel, die zu dieser Debatte beigetragen haben, sind bei Redwood, a. a. O., S. 50–90, wiedergegeben.

[7] Die Zitate in diesem Abschnitt sind von Elgar selbst. Zur ausführlicheren Diskussion der außermusikalischen Bezüge in den *Enigma-Variationen* vgl. Lan Parrott, *Elgar*, London 1971, Kapitel 7.

seiner Freunde, seine Gattin und sich selbst auf kompositorische Weise:

I. (C.A.E.) Elgars Gattin Alice
II. (H.D.S-P.) Hew David Steuart-Powell, Pianist im Trio mit Elgar und Basil Nevison. Diese Variation porträtiert seine „charakteristischen diatonischen Läufe durch die Tonarten".
III. (R.B.T.) Richard Baxter Townshend, ein Exzentriker aus Oxford; dieser Abschnitt spiegelt seine „tiefe Stimme" wider, die „gelegentlich ins Sopran-Timbre umschlägt".
IV. (W.M.B.) William Meath Baker, der „[…] den Tagesplan verlas und unverzüglich den Proberaum mit einem lässigen Türknall verließ".
V. (R.P.A.) Richard Penrose Arnold, Sohn des Dichters Matthew Arnold, „wunderlich und geistreich".
VI. (Ysobel) Isabel Fitton, eine Bratscherin, die Läufe auf ihrem Instrument zu üben hatte.
VII. (Troyte) Arthur Troyte Griffith: die Pauken geben seine „linkischen Versuche" wieder, „das Klavier zu spielen".
VIII. (W.N.) Winifred Norbury: diese Variation ist ein Spiegelbild ihres friedvollen Hauses aus dem 18. Jahrhundert.
IX. (Nimrod) August Johannes Jaeger (Jäger = Nimrod); Elgar schrieb an ihn, „ich habe Ihre Extravaganzen beiseite gelassen und die gute, liebenswerte SEELE in Ihrer Brust gesehen".
X. (Dorabella) Dora Penny. Elgars Kosename für sie war Dorabella; er gab dazu die Erklärung, dieser Name wäre ein Zitat aus Mozarts *Così fan tutte*. Im Übrigen stotterte sie.
XI. (G.R.S.) George Robertson Sinclair, 1899 designierter Organist in der Kathedrale von Hereford. „Diese Variation hat nichts mit Orgeln oder Kathedralen zu tun und mit G.R.S. auch nur am Rande. Die ersten Takte sind auf seine riesige Bulldogge Dan zurückzuführen".
XII. (B.G.N.) Basil Nevison. „Mein Tribut an einen sehr lieben Freund."

XIII. (***) Diese Variation hat Elgar nur mit Sternchen überschrieben. Er ließ es zu, dass seine Biographen vermuteten, Lady Mary Lygon, eine Freundin in musikalischen Dingen, sei die Widmungsträgerin. Tatsächlich notierte Elgar in seinem Konzept zum Verzeichnis der Variationen für die 1913 veröffentlichten Notizen ursprünglich die Initialen L. M. L. vorneweg.[8] Kürzlich wurde die Vermutung ausgesprochen, dass die musikalisch verewigte Person die schöne, glanzvolle Amerikanerin Julia Worthington sei, die Elgars heimliche Liebe gewesen sein könnte.[9] Das häufig in der Klarinette zu hörende Zitat aus Mendelssohn Bartholdys *Meeresstille und glückliche Fahrt*, op. 27, verwirrt eher.
XIV. (E.D.U.) Dies ist der Komponist selber; unter dem Namen Edu war er Alice vertraut.

Im Hinblick auf den engen Zusammenhang zu Elgars epigrammatischen Bezügen auf die Rätsel in seinen Variationen ist es sinnvoll, des Komponisten eigene Gefühle ihnen gegenüber in Erinnerung zu rufen:

im künstlerischen oder musikalischen Sinne springt gar nichts dabei heraus, wenn man hinter das Rätsel mancher Personen kommt; der Zuhörer sollte die Musik als solche hören und sich nicht mit wie auch immer gearteten Verzwicktheiten eines „Programms" belasten. Für mich waren die unterschiedlichen Persönlichkeiten eine Quelle der Inspiration und deren Idealisierung ein Vergnügen – ein Vergnügen, das sich über die Jahre noch verstärkt hat.[10]

Die Erstausgabe der Partitur erschien bei Novello in London im Jahre 1899. Die autographe Partitur wird in der British Library unter *GB-Lbl* Add. MS 59004 aufbewahrt.

Esther Cavett-Dunshy
Übersetzung: Norbert Henning

---

[8] Edward Elgar, *My Friends Pictured Within*, London 1913.
[9] Nicholas Reed, „Elgar's Enigmatic Inamorata", in: *The Musical Times*, Bd. CXXV/1698, August 1954, S. 430–434.
[10] Maine, a. a. O., *The Works*, S. 102.

PRÉFACE

Deux jours après avoir inscrit : « Achevé le 19 février 1899 » sur le manuscrit autographe de ses *Variations on an Original Theme for Orchestra* (*Variations sur un thème original pour orchestre*), op.36, Edward Elgar adressa sa partition au célèbre chef d'orchestre wagnérien Hans Richter, connu pour ne diriger que des œuvres qu'il tenait en haute estime. Or les *Variations* figurèrent au programme de son concert londonien suivant, le 19 juin 1899 et l'œuvre, qui fut accueillie avec enthousiasme, est restée l'une des favorites du répertoire orchestral. Ce fut un aboutissement remarquable de la part d'Elgar, alors que, de tout le règne de la reine Victoria, aucune œuvre orchestrale anglaise n'avait suscité une telle attention de la communauté musicale. A la suite de sa première exécution, August Jaeger, ami proche et mentor d'Elgar représenté dans la variation « Nimrod », écrivit à Elgar qu'il trouvait le Finale trop court. Malgré sa réticence à tout changement, expliquant que la tonalité de *sol* majeur était « épuisée » et « qu'une réexposition [du thème] ne conviendrait pas », Elgar compléta le mouvement de cent mesures après la mesure 76 au cours des semaines suivantes et assura à Jaeger qu'il était satisfait du nouvel « appendice » de l'œuvre.[1]

Le succès des *Variations*, qui furent jouées à travers l'Europe et jusqu'en la Russie en 1904, ne marqua pas seulement une percée de la musique anglaise, mais aussi, pour Elgar, un accomplissement personnel qui détermina les débuts de sa renommée internationale. Il avait acquis une réputation au niveau national durant la décennie précédant la composition des *Variations* grâce à des œuvres pour chœur et orchestre montées lors de festivals en Angleterre, principalement *The Black Knight* (*Le chevalier noir*) (1892), *The Light of Life* (*La lumière de la vie*) (1896), *King Olaf* (1896) et *Caractacus*

(1898). Un commentateur observa que la plus grande énigme de l'œuvre résidait dans le fait qu'elle émanât d'un compositeur qui, jusqu'à l'âge de quarante-deux ans, n'avait pas produit de chef-d'œuvre.[2] Un autre avança, en dépit du rapport peu classique régissant le thème et les variations d'Elgar, qu'après ses œuvres chorales « vaguement narratives », celui-ci avait réalisé son besoin de la « discipline » impliquée par la variation.[3]

En 1904, son anoblissement contribua à donner d'Elgar l'image du plus « anglais » des compositeurs, or cette représentation demeure paradoxale dans la mesure où le génie singulier d'Elgar transcenda la musique de ses prédécesseurs et contemporains anglais, plutôt qu'il ne s'en nourrit, et où ses successeurs soit adaptèrent (Bliss, Walton), soit rejetèrent (Holst, Vaughan Williams) ses techniques formelles et compositionnelles explicitement rattachées au XIXème siècle. Ceci ne signifie en rien que ne figure aucune tendance novatrice dans la musique d'Elgar. Richard Strauss le considéra « le premier musicien anglais progressiste ».

Les influences étrangères sont facilement identifiables dans les *Variations*. Ainsi, par exemple, la question de leur forme mérite qu'on s'y arrête. Après que les compositeurs viennois eurent écrit des séries de variations comme *finale* de symphonies (Haydn, Beethoven) ou de concertos (Mozart), le genre des variations orchestrales indépendantes apparut au cours du XIXème siècle. Peut-être Elgar eut-il à l'esprit les *Symphonic Variations* de l'anglais Parry (1897) pendant son travail, mais les modèles de variations orchestrales ou de variations pour orchestre et instrument soliste de Brahms, Dvoák, Franck et Tchaïkovski étaient certes

---

[1] Basil MAINE, *Elgar : his Life and works*, 2 vol., Londres, 1933, *The Life*, pp.86/87

[2] Jack WESTRUP, « The Enigma III » *in* : Christopher REDWOOD (éd.), *An Elgar Companion*, Londres, 1982, p.85

[3] Diana M. McVEAGH, « Elgar » *in* : Stanley SADIE (éd) *The New Grove Dictionary of Music and Musicians*, vol.6, Londres, 1980, p.121

plus largement célèbres. Il se peut également, au vu des incontestables associations extra-musicales de l'œuvre, que les poèmes symphoniques de Liszt, Smetana et Richard Strauss, entre autres, aient exercé un effet incitatif sur les *Variations*, sans oublier les cryptogrammes de Schumann et, surtout, les drames en musique de Wagner.

Elgar dédia son œuvre « à mes amis portraiturés dans cette musique » et ajouta le mot « Enigma » au-dessus de la musique sur la première page du manuscrit autographe de la grande partition. C'est ainsi que les *Variations* acquièrent leur notoriété de *Enigma Variations* (*Variations énigmatiques*), bien qu'Elgar ne les ait jamais évoquées sous ce titre dans sa correspondance. Quelle est donc cette énigme ? La curiosité fut d'emblée éveillée par les notes écrites par Elgar pour le programme du concert au cours duquel fut créée l'œuvre :

L'Enigme, je ne la dévoilerai pas – son « discours obscur » doit rester inexpliqué et je vous préviens que le lien apparent entre les variations et le thème est souvent de la nature la plus ténue ; par ailleurs, à travers la série dans son ensemble, un autre thème plus ample « court » mais il n'est pas joué.[4]

Elgar manifesta une détermination grandissante à ne pas fournir d'indices ou à donner des réponses ambiguës à ceux qui pensaient avoir élucidé le mystère. Le « discours obscur » fut interprété de diverses manières. On le dit évoquer le « caractère élégiaque » du thème et le sentiment de solitude de l'artiste au cours de la composition des *Variations*. Il aurait également pu refléter la vision qu'Elgar avait de lui-même (« exactement comme moi et mon influence sur tout le monde – toujours mauvais »)[5] à en croire le rythme de la phrase initiale reprenant celui de la prononciation normale du nom d'Edward Elgar. Les *Variations* furent peut-être même inspirées par un passage extrait de la version de la *Vulgate* des Epîtres aux Corinthiens dont

l'une des traductions anglaises contient le mot « dark » (obscur).

Le « thème plus ample » qui « court » serait un thème qui n'est jamais énoncé mais serait un contrepoint implicite au thème existant. L'air de *Auld Lang Syne* (*Ce n'est qu'un au-revoir*) a été le plus souvent cité, à coté de nombreuses autres suggestions. Certains spécialistes sont réservés quant à cette approche car un air caché coïncidant avec le thème aurait peu de chance de correspondre à toutes les variations et parce que la déclaration d'Elgar ne suppose pas nécessairement que ce « thème plus ample » se rapporte à une mélodie spécifique. Il pourrait renvoyer à une amitié (pour laquelle *Auld Lang Syne* semblerait convenir) ou rappeler une expérience musicale plus générale comme celle de la musique de J.S. Bach, Elgar ayant peut-être délibérément inséré le nom de Bach dans le thème qui commence par B (*si* bémol) et se termine pas H (*si* bécarre) entre lesquels un A (*la*) et C (*do*) sont marqués *tenuto*.[6]

S'il paraît peu vraisemblable que les différents aspects de l'énigme des *Variations* soient résolus un jour, Elgar révéla, en revanche, volontiers l'identité de ses « amis portraiturés dans cette musique », sous forme d'initiales ou de pseudonymes inscrits dans la partition au-dessus de chacune des variations.[7] Il esquissa les portraits musicaux de douze de ses amis, de son épouse et de lui-même :

I. (C.A.E.) Alice, l'épouse d'Elgar.
II. (H.D.S-P.) Hew David Steuart-Powell, le pianiste du trio formé avec Elgar et Basil Nevison. La variation dépeint ses « traits diatoniques caractéristiques sur les touches ».
III. (R.B.T.) Richard Baxter Townshend, universitaire excentrique d'Oxford. Cette section rappelle « sa voix grave s'envolant, à l'occasion, vers un timbre de *soprano* ».

4 D.M. POWELL, *Edward Elgar: Memories of a Variation*, Londres, 1937, (3e éd.) 1949, p.121
5 Michael KENNEDY, *Elgar Orchestral Music*, London, 1970, p.22
6 Cinq articles importants ayant contribué à ce débat sont reproduits *in* : REDWOOD, *op. cit.*, pp.50–90
7 Les citations de ce paragraphe sont dues à Elgar lui-même. Pour une analyse plus détaillée des références extra-musicales présentes dans les *Variations*, voir : Ian PARROTT, *Elgar*, Londres, 1971, chapitre 7

IV. (W.M.B.) William Meath Baker qui « [...] lut à haute voix le programme du jour et quitta soudainement la salle de musique en claquant la porte sans y prendre garde ».

V. (R.P.A) Richard Penrose Arnold, fils du poète Matthew Arnold, « plaisant et spirituel ».

VI. (Ysobel) Isabel Fitton, altiste qui devait travailler les sauts de cordes.

VII. (Troyte) Arthur Troyte Griffith. Les tambours représentent ses « essais maladroits de jouer du pianoforte ».

VIII. (W.N.) Winifred Norbury. Cette variation est en fait une description de sa paisible maison du XVIIIème siècle.

IX. (Nimrod) August Johannes Jaeger (*Jaeger* = chasseur en allemand, d'où « Nimrod » [personnage biblique de chasseur]). Elgar écrivit à Jaeger : « J'ai écarté vos manières extérieures et n'ai vu que l'âme bonne, aimable et honnête au-dedans de vous. »

X. (Dorabella) Dora Penny, surnommée Dorabella par Elgar qui expliquait que ce surnom était une citation de *Così fan tutte* de Mozart, et atteinte de bégaiement.

XI. (G.R.S.) George Robertson Sinclair, nommé organiste titulaire de la cathédrale de Hereford en 1899. « La variation n'a rien à voir avec les orgues, les cathédrales ou, sauf de très loin, avec G.R.S. Les premières mesures furent inspirées par Dan, son grand bulldog. »

XII. (B.G.N.) Basil Nevison. « Hommage à un ami très cher. »

XIII. (***) Unique variation surmontée d'astérisques. Elgar laissa ses biographes supposer que sa dédicataire était Lady Mary Lygon, amie musicienne, au vu des initiales L.M.L. placées en tête de son commentaire de cette variation dans le brouillon des notes qu'il publia en 1913.[8] Une suggestion plus récente avance que la personne enchâssée dans cette variation serait la belle et brillante américaine Julia Worthington, possible amour secret d'Elgar.[9] La citation lancinante de clarinette extraite de l'opus 27 de Mendelssohn, *Mer calme et voyage heureux*, contribue sans doute au mystère.

XIV. (E.D.U.) représente le compositeur lui-même. Edu était le nom que lui donnait Alice.

Face aux indéniables questions soulevées par les références épigrammatiques d'Elgar quant au mystère de ses *Variations*, il n'est pas inutile de rappeler les sentiments du compositeur à ce sujet :

Il n'y a rien à gagner, au sens artistique ou musical, à la résolution de l'énigme d'aucune des personnalités ; l'auditeur devrait écouter la musique comme de la musique et ne pas se préoccuper des subtilités d'un « programme ». Pour moi, les différentes personnalités ont été une source d'inspiration et leur idéalisation un plaisir – qui s'intensifie avec les années.[10]

La partition des *Variations* fut publiée pour la première fois par Novello à Londres en 1899. Le manuscrit autographe d'Elgar de la grande partition est conservé à la British Library.

Esther Cavett-Dunsby
Traduction : Agnès Ausseur

8 Edward ELGAR, *My Friends Pictured Within*, Londres, 1913
9 Nicholas REED, Elgar's « Enigmatic Inamorata », *in*: *The Musical Times*, vol.CXXV/1968, août 1984, pp.430/434
10 MAINE, *op. cit.*, *The Works*, p.102

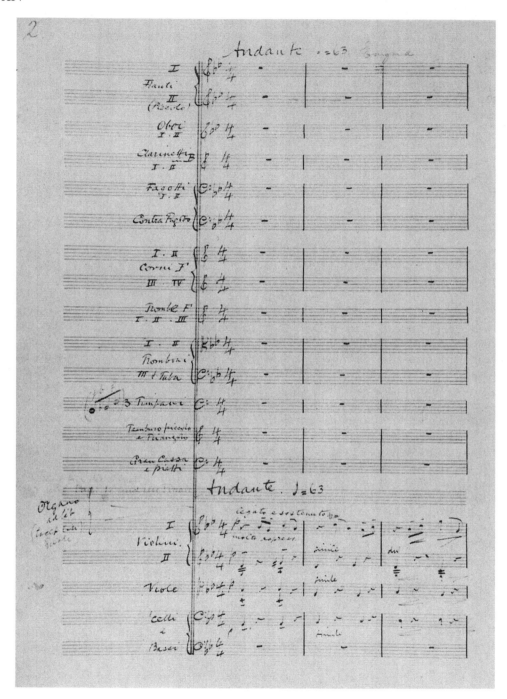

From the autograph score
Aus dem Autograph der Partitur
De l'autograph de la partition

VARIATIONS
Enigma

Edward Elgar
(1857–1934)
Op. 36

No. 884   EE 6801

2

4

I.
(C.A.E.)

8

II.
(H.D.S-P.)

(C.Fg.)

(C. Fg.)

20

IV.
(W. M. B.)

24

V.
(R. P. A.)

(Din G alta.)

attacca.

attacca.

VI.
(Ysobel.)

VII.
(Troyte.)

36

40

27

46

VIII.
(W.N.)

52

IX.
(Nimrod.)

34

54

X.
(Dorabella.)
Intermezzo.

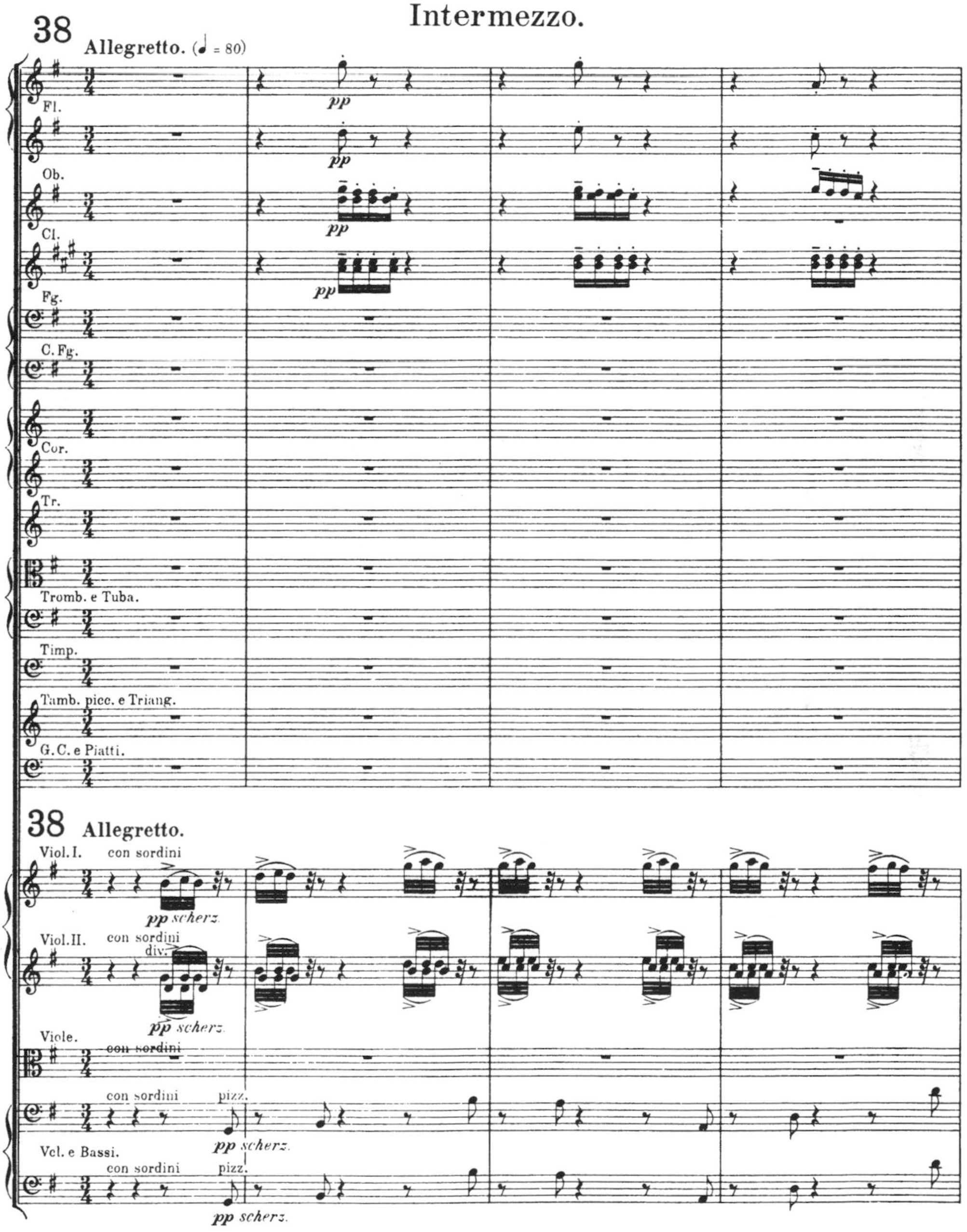

40

41

66

72

74

51

81

82

53

84

86

*) Dieser Takt wird nur im Falle einer Separat
Aufführung dieser Var. XII gespielt.

*) This bar should be omitted except
when Var. XII is played separately.

XIII.
(***)
Romanza.

88

60
poco rall. molto tranquillo

60
poco rall. molto tranquillo

XIV.
(E.D.U.)
Finale.

a tempo (primo)

a tempo (primo)

67

67

74 animando

74 animando

116

accel. poco a poco **77**

accel. poco a poco **77**

(mit Metall Schlägel)
Struck with metal beater

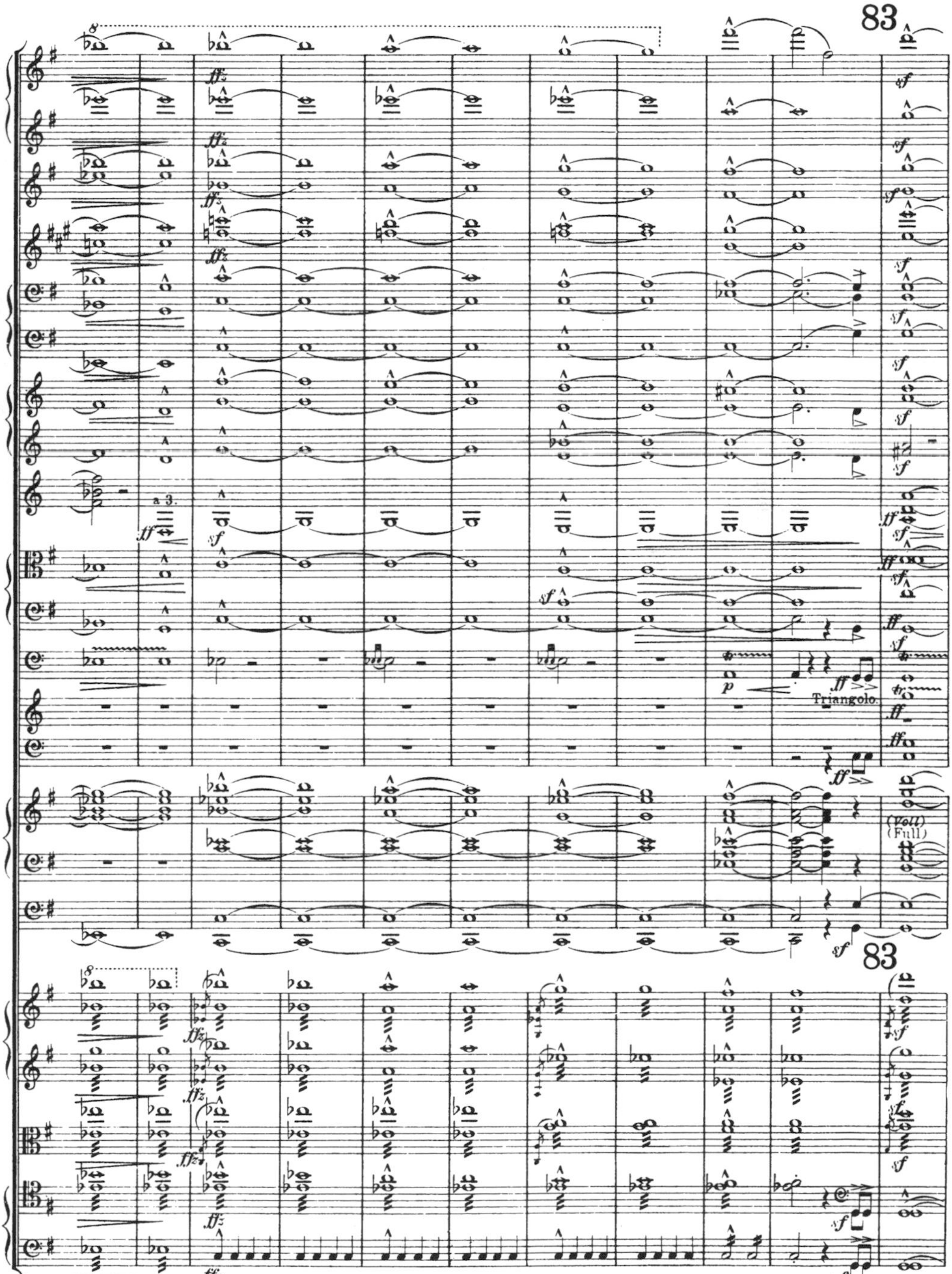
83
a 3.
Triangolo.
(Voll)
(Full)
83

(1899.)